The GH Book

by Lynn Maslen Kertell
pictures by Sue Hendra and John R. Maslen

Scholastic Inc.

New York • Toronto • London • Auckland • Sydney • Mexico City • New Delhi • Hong Kong • Buenos Aires

Grapes

goat

Here's a glorious gift for goose.

Goat, no gobbling!

Hole

hamsters

Who is hiding in the big hat?

Horse, hawk, hippo, or hamster?

Goose looks grand

in her handsome new hat.

Look for these **g** and **h** words in this book.

gift	hamster(s)
glorious	handsome
goat	hat
gobbling	hawk
goose	hiding
grand	hippo
grapes	hole
	horse

Look for these additional **g** and **h** words in the pictures: gingerbread man, grapevine, grass, grasshopper, hatband, heart, hooves, horns, and hummingbird.